MAXIMUM
RIDE

WHAT CAME BEFORE

Max and her flock are genetic experiments. Created by a mysterious lab known only as the "School," their genetic codes have been spliced with avian DNA, giving them wings and the power to soar. What they lack are homes, families, and memories of a real life.

The flock's long battle against ITEX — the corporation behind their creation — and its "By-Half" initiative that sought to wipe out half the world's population came to a head in Germany. Though Max and the girls emerged on top with the help of kids across the world, their victory came at a price: Ari sacrificed himself to protect Max, his half-sister. Enraged, Max made short work of ITEX's latest mutation and her "fake" mother and the facility's director, Marian Janssen.

With nowhere else to turn, Max and the flock are welcomed with open arms at the home of Valencia Martinez — Max's biological mother — in Arizona. But they were granted only a few short weeks of reprieve before Jeb turned up with an offer of aid and protection from the government higher-ups. Skeptical, Max agreed to a meeting, but when the talk turned toward building a special "school" where the flock could be studied, Max was quick to walk out the door, leery of their intentions.

Following her instincts, Max led the flock to a remote desert area where they reunited with none other than Dr. Martinez. On her recommendation the flock agreed to assist the scientists aboard the *Wendy K* in their research into the effects of global warming. But their Antarctic peace was shattered when the flock was kidnapped by Gozen and the Über-Director!

Almost auctioned off to the highest bidder, the flock was saved in the nick of time by a Category 5 hurricane. But even traveling through the eye of the storm didn't prepare Max for her biggest challenge yet — giving a speech in front of the entire U.S. Congress about the immediate dangers of global warming.

But the world isn't saved just quite yet, and following the voice in her head, Max and the flock take off to a whole new adventure!

CHARACTER INTRODUCTION

MAXIMUM RIDE

Max is the eldest member of the flock, and the responsibility of caring for her comrades has fallen to her. Tough and uncompromising, she's willing to put everything on the line to protect her "family."

FANG

Only slightly younger than Max, Fang is one of the elder members of the flock. Cool and reliable, Fang is Max's rock. He may be the strongest of them all, but most of the time it is hard to figure out what is on his mind.

IGGY

Being blind doesn't mean that Iggy is helpless. He has not only an incredible sense of hearing, but also a particular knack (and fondness) for explosives.

NUDGE

Motormouth Nudge would probably spend most days at the mall if not for her pesky mutant-bird-girl-being-hunted-by-wolf-men problem.

GASMAN

The name pretty much says it all. The Gasman (or Gazzy) has the art of flatulence down to a science. He's also Angel's biological big brother.

ANGEL

The youngest member of the flock and Gazzy's little sister, Angel seems to have some peculiar abilities — mind reading, for example.

ARI

Just seven years old, Ari is Jeb's son but was transformed into an Eraser. He used to have an axe to grind with Max but ends up losing his life protecting her.

JEB BATCHELDER

The flock's former benefactor, Jeb was a scientist at the School before helping the flock to make their original escape.

MAXIMUM RIDE

ONE—
TWO—
SWOOP!!

MAXIMUM RIDE

CHAPTER 53

GAZZY! STICK TO THE CHO-REOGRA-PHY!
SHOOOM
HEY! WATCH GRAVITY IN ACTION!
THIS IS A PAYING JOB! DON'T BLOW IT!
FWIP
HMPH...
IT'S JUST DONUTS ...

THAT'S RIGHT. WE'RE PERFORMING IN AN AIR SHOW.
AND THEY'RE PAYING US MOSTLY IN DONUTS.

I WASN'T SURE ABOUT THIS WHOLE AIR-SHOW THING TO BEGIN WITH...
...BUT HOW COULD I REFUSE MY OWN MOM?
AFTER OUR LAST "WORKING VACATION" IN ANT-FREAKING-ARCTICA, MY MOM AND A BUNCH OF SCIENTISTS CREATED AN ORGANIZATION CALLED THE COALITION TO STOP THE MADNESS, OR CSM.
BASICALLY, THEY'RE TRYING TO TELL THE WHOLE WORLD ABOUT THE DANGERS OF POLLUTION, GREENHOUSE GASES, DEPENDENCE ON FOREIGN OIL—YOU GET THE PICTURE.
WOO-HOO!!
A MEMBER OF THE CSM CAME UP WITH THE IDEA OF A TRAVELING AIR SHOW TO REALLY GET THE MESSAGE OUT.
HANGING OUT WITH THE CSM FOLKS HAS SOME BENEFITS, CHIEFLY FOOD AND DECENT PLACES TO SLEEP.
AND BEST OF ALL...
...I CAN SEE MY MOM MORE OFTEN.

HEY!
YOU ENJOYING BEING A SPOKES-FREAK?
!
SWISH
SHRUG
IT'S A JOB.

YEP. SO LONG AS THEY DON'T WORRY ABOUT PESKY CHILD LABOR LAWS...
OOF!
WHAM

WHAT ARE YOU DOING, GOOFBALL?
THIS ISN'T PLAYTIME—

!!
FWP

WOOF!
TOTAL!

SCATTER!
GET OUT OF FIRING RANGE!

TOTAL!
I'M HIT, MAX.
THEY GOT ME.
I GUESS I'M GONNA LIVE FAST, DIE YOUNG...
...AND LEAVE A BEAUTIFUL CORPSE, HUH?

WH- WHERE DID THEY HIT YOU, TOTAL?
HUH?

TELL AKILA...
...TELL HER SHE'S ALWAYS BEEN THE ONLY ONE...

THE ONLY ONE...?

TOTAL?
YES?

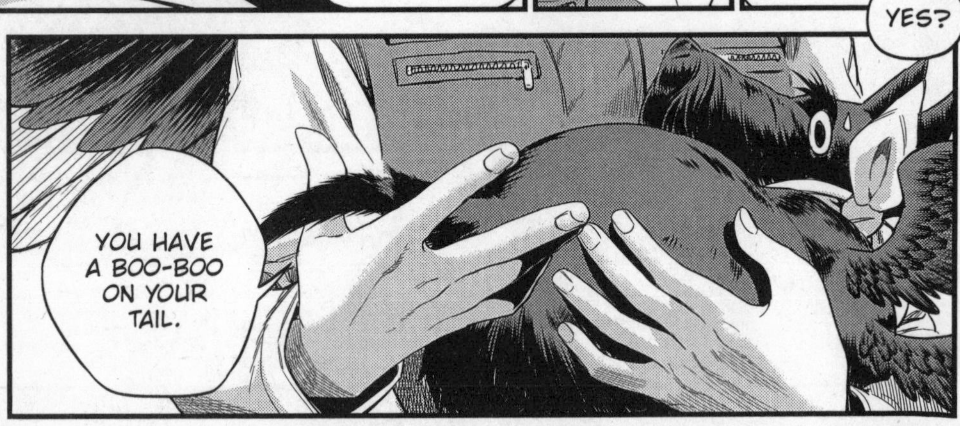
YOU HAVE A BOO-BOO ON YOUR TAIL.

I THINK A BAND-AID IS PROBABLY ALL YOU NEED.
I... I'M HIT!
I'M BLEED-ING!
THOSE SCOUNDRELS WILL PAY FOR THIS!
HOW'S HE DOING?

......
WAG
WAG

HE NEEDS A BAND-AID.
FOUND YOUR SNIPER.
ONE SNIPER OR A WHOLE FLOTILLA?
ONLY SEE THE ONE.
SO WHAT, WE'RE NOT WORTH A WHOLE FLOTILLA ANYMORE?
FLAP FLAP
WHAT'S UP?
WINGS OUT, SPUD. GO FLY ON YOUR OWN.
IS TOTAL OKAY?
TOTAL'S OKAY. BUT THERE'S ONE SNIPER BELOW. NOW WE GOTTA GO TAKE HIM OUT.

FLASH
FWOOSH
SHOOOM
THERE HE IS...
HEH...
CLICK

KA-BOOM!!!

THREE DAYS LATER...

HOLLYWOOD

HELLO! COME IN, GUYS!
A MEMBER OF THE CSM HAD A FRIEND WHO HAD A COUSIN WHO WAS MARRIED TO SOMEONE WHO KNOWS SOMEONE AT A HOLLYWOOD AGENCY—
I'M SHARON. WELCOME!

COME IN! COME IN! I'M STEVE BLACKMAN.
MAX! MAY I CALL YOU MAX?
NO.
BLUNT...

SWEAT...

WELL!
LET'S SIT DOWN, HUH?
CLAP!
WE'RE ALWAYS HUNGRY.
YOU KIDS THIRSTY? HUNGRY?

AH— YES, OF COURSE! GROWING KIDS!
JEFF?
FLIP!
YES, SIR.
ROLL ROLL

WHOA!!

......
NOM
NOM

NOW, SHALL WE GET DOWN TO BUSINESS?
YOU KIDS...

...WANT TO BE BIG STARS, EH?
PFFFT
YES?!

GOD, NO!
NO WAY!!
ABSOLUTELY NOT!

Y-YOU KNOW...
...MODELS?
AIEEE
TWING!
ACTORS?

NOPE.
MAX, I MEAN— MAX.
YOU'RE SELLING YOURSELF SHORT.
YOU GUYS CAN DO ANY-THING, BE ANYTHING.
YOU WANT YOUR OWN MOVIE? FLOCK ACTION FIGURES?
I WANT TO BE AN ACTION FIGURE!
OH! THEN DO YOU LIKE THIS?
I'LL GIVE IT TO YOU AS A PRESENT.
WHOA —!
GOOD ... THEY'RE JUST KIDS.
HEY, I DIDN'T CATCH EVERYONE'S NAMES.
WHAT'S YOUR NAME, SWEET-HEART?
SSK...
ISABELLA VON FRANKENSTEIN ROTHSCHILD.
PICK

SORRY— THAT WAS... ISABELLA VON...?
......
YOU GOT YOUR SHOES ON EBAY.
BUT YOU'RE RIGHT.
IT DOESN'T MAKE SENSE TO GO RETAIL...
...NOT ON WHAT SKINFLINT STEVE PAYS YOU.
BLUSH!
AHEM—

SILENCE...
AH, HUH.
HOW ABOUT YOU, SON?
YOU WANT TO BE AN ACTION FIGURE, RIGHT?
NOD NOD NOD
YEAH!! YEAH!!
WHAT'S YOUR NAME?

THEY CALL ME THE SHARK-ALATOR!
FWIP
THE... SHARK-ALATOR ...?

I'M CINNAMON.
CINNAMON ALLSPICE LA FEVER.
NOM
NOM
THIS SHRIMP IS AWESOME!

THEY CALL ME THE WHITE KNIGHT.
OH? WHY IS THAT?
UGH—

THEY'RE NOT GONNA CALL ME THE BLACK KNIGHT.

HMPH...

BOLT

......
MY NAME IS FANG.
WIPE...
AND I'M OUTTA HERE.
AH— WAIT—!

OPEN

WAIT, MAX—
LET'S GO.

THANKS.
BUT NO THANKS.

FWOOSH

HOTEL
ALL I'M SAYING IS—
WOULD GOING ON OPRAH JUST ONCE BE THE END OF THE ENTIRE WORLD?

NO, BUT...
I WANT TO BE AN ACTION FIGURE!
SIGH...
GUYS...

REMEMBER FOUR DAYS AGO?
THE BULLETS WHIZZING PAST...
...THE SNIPER...
...THE EXPLODING BUILDING?

I CERTAINLY HAVEN'T FORGOTTEN!
WAG
WAG

MY POINT IS THAT...
...CLEARLY, SOMEONE IS STILL AFTER US, STILL WANTS US DEAD.
YES, OUR AIR SHOWS FOR THE CSM ARE BIG HITS.
THERE ARE PEOPLE WHO ARE SORT OF ACCEPTING US AS BEING... DIFFERENT.

BUT WE'RE STILL IN DANGER.
WE'LL ALWAYS BE IN DANGER.
I'M TIRED OF BEING IN DANGER!

TEARY
I HATE THIS!
TEARY
I JUST WANT TO—

SILENCE...

FWUMP

WE ALL HATE THIS.
BUT UNTIL SOMEONE CAN PROVE TO ME BEYOND A DOUBT THAT WE'RE SAFE...
...I HAVE TO MAKE DECISIONS THAT WILL KEEP US MORE OR LESS IN ONE PIECE. I KNOW IT SUCKS.
SPEAKING OF THINGS SUCKING...
I LIKE THE AIR SHOWS.
...I SAY WE DITCH THE AIR SHOWS COMPLETELY.

I LIKE THE AIR SHOWS TOO.
THEY MAKE ME FEEL LIKE A FAMOUS MOVIE STAR.
THEY'RE NOT SAFE.
I'M TORN...

THE SNIPER WHO SHOT AT ME TURNED OUT TO BE A NEW FORM OF CYBORG/HUMAN.
THE BUILDING DIDN'T ACTUALLY EXPLODE BECAUSE WE WERE CLOSE—THE SNIPER BLEW HIMSELF UP INSTEAD OF LETTING US SEE HIM.
KA-CHAK...
THAT'S DEDICATION FOR YA. THAT THING DIDN'T GRAFT THAT GUN TO HIS ARM BY HIMSELF. SOMEONE MADE HIM.
ON THE OTHER HAND... THE CSM'S REALLY COUNTING ON US TO CONTINUE THE AIR SHOWS.
SO FAR THEY'VE BEEN BIG SUCCESSES, AND THE CSM HAS BEEN ABLE TO HAND OUT TONS OF EDUCATIONAL CARDS ABOUT POLLUTION...

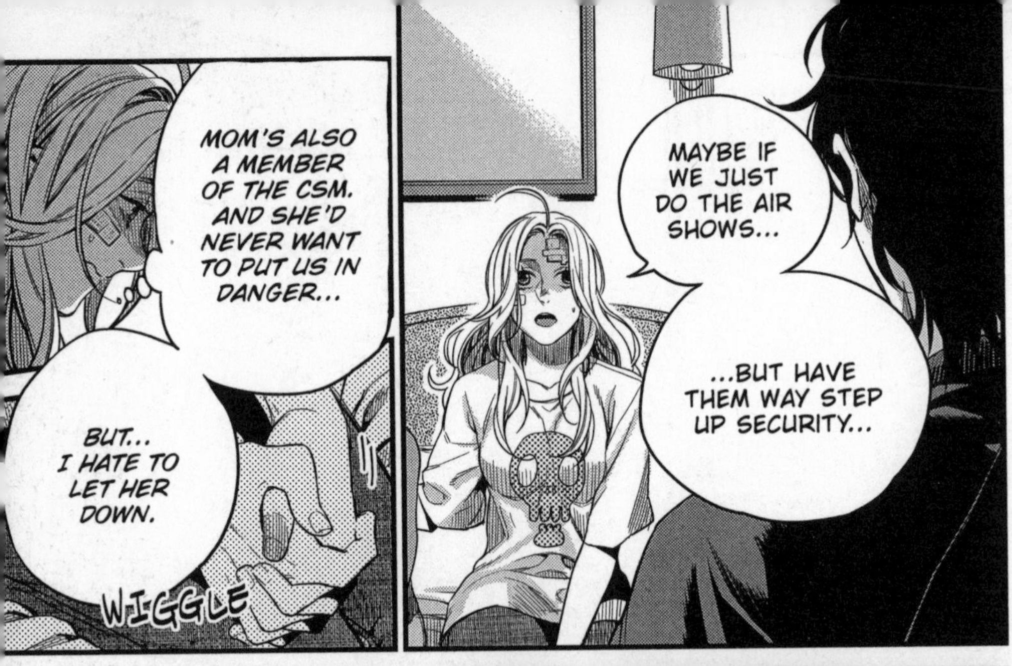
MOM'S ALSO A MEMBER OF THE CSM. AND SHE'D NEVER WANT TO PUT US IN DANGER...
BUT... I HATE TO LET HER DOWN.
WIGGLE
MAYBE IF WE JUST DO THE AIR SHOWS...
...BUT HAVE THEM WAY STEP UP SECURITY...

NO.
FLAT

BOLT!
WHAT?
SSK...
SSK...
SSK...

THE AIR SHOWS ARE TOO DANGEROUS.

ONE MORE SHOW.

CLENCH!

I CAN'T LET MY MOM DOWN.

SSSK...
ALL RIGHT.

HUH?!

CSM...?
YOU'RE RIGHT.
WE DON'T WANT TO LET THE CSM DOWN.

OH. RIGHT. DR. BRIGID DWYER IS ALSO PART OF THE CSM...
...AND SHE PLANNED ON MEETING US AT OUR NEXT SHOW IN MEXICO CITY.

GRIT...

?

OKAY...
SLAM!

AAAAAAH!
SHAAAAAAA

MAXIMUM RIDE

I GREW UP WITH FANG, FROM THE VERY BEGINNING...

...WHEN OUR DOG CRATES WERE STACKED NEXT TO EACH OTHER IN THE LAB OF EXPERIMENTAL HORROR THAT WE CALLED THE SCHOOL.

MAXIMUM RIDE
CHAPTER 54

HEN WE'D BEEN RESCUED BY OUR BAD GUY, TURNED GOOD GUY, TURNED BAD AGAIN, TURNED I DON'T KNOW WHAT LATELY—AND FANG AND I HAD BEEN LIKE BROTHER AND SISTER WITH THE REST OF THE FLOCK, HIDDEN AWAY IN THE COLORADO MOUNTAINS.

THEN JEB (SEE DESCRIPTION ABOVE) DISAPPEARED, AND I BECAME FLOCK LEADER. MAYBE BECAUSE I WAS THE OLDEST. OR THE MOST RUTHLESS. OR THE MOST ORGANIZED. I DON'T KNOW. BUT I WAS THE FLOCK LEADER, AND FANG WAS MY RIGHT WINGMAN.

BUT THIS PAST YEAR, THINGS STARTED TO CHANGE.

FANG HAD BEEN INTERESTED IN A GIRL...

...AND I'D HATED IT.

I'D HAD MY FIRST DATE WITH A GUY...

...AND FANG HAD HATED IT.

THEN, LAST MONTH, HE'D GOTTEN ALL COZY WITH DR. BRIGID DWYER, THE TWENTY-ONE-YEAR-OLD SCIENTIST.

AND—GET THIS—SHE'D SORT OF FLIRTED BACK WITH HIM.

AND HE'S—PRACTICALLY—JUST A KID!

IN THE MIDST OF ALL THIS, FANG KISSED ME.

SEVERAL TIMES...

SO NOW I'M FREAKED AND TEMPTED AND TERRIFIED AND WORRIED AND LONGING...
...AND ALSO ANGRY AT HIM FOR EVEN STARTING THIS WHOLE THING TO BEGIN WITH.
BRUSH
BRUSH
A YEAR AGO THE ONLY THING IMPORTANT ABOUT MY CLOTHES WAS WHETHER I COULD FIGHT IN THEM...
...AND WHEN MY HAIR GOT IN MY EYES, I HACKED IT OFF WITH A KNIFE.

AND FANG HAD BEEN MY BEST FRIEND AND AN EXCELLENT FIGHTER.
NOW EVERY-THING'S UPSIDE DOWN.

TUG
TUG
IF I... BRAID MY HAIR LIKE THIS...
...AM I PRETTY TOO?
SHUDDER!!
YOU ARE REALLY PRETTY, MAX.
FWIP
FWIP
WAY TO GO, ACE...
...HAVE EMBARRASSING PERSONAL THOUGHTS WHILE YOU'RE TWO FEET FROM A MIND READER.
YOU HAVE NICE HAIR...
...AND REALLY PRETTY EYES.

YEAH. BROWN AND BROWN.
AND YOUR EYES ARE LIKE—
YOU KNOW THOSE CHOCOLATES WE HAD IN FRANCE?
NO, YOUR HAIR HAS LITTLE SUN STREAKS IN IT.
WITH THE GOOEY STUFF IN THE MIDDLE, WITH THE ALCOHOL IN 'EM EXCEPT WE DIDN'T KNOW...
...AND GAZZY ATE A MILLION AND THEN BARFED ALL NIGHT?
THE COLOR OF MY EYES IS LIKE BARFED-UP CHOCOLATE?
NO, THE CHOCOLATES BEFORE THEY WERE BARFED.
MAX...
...YOU KNOW FANG IS THE BEST GUY EVER.
AND HE LOVES YOU.
'COS YOU'RE THE BEST GIRL EVER.

WE ALL LOVE EACH OTHER, ANGEL.
NO, NOT LIKE THIS.
BLUSH!
FANG LOVES YOU.

OKAY, MAYBE I'LL GIVE HIM A BREAK.
TURN
MAYBE YOU SHOULD GIVE HIM MORE THAN THAT.
HE COULD TOTALLY BE YOUR BOY-FRIEND.
YOU GUYS COULD GET MARRIED.

I'M ONLY A KID!
I CAN'T GET MARRIED!
BOLT!
YOU COULD IN NEW HAMP-SHIRE.
HOW DOES SHE KNOW THIS STUFF?
FORGET IT!
NO ONE'S GETTING MARRIED!

NOW GO TO SLEEP, BEFORE I KILL YOU!
NOT IN NEW HAMPSHIRE OR ANYWHERE ELSE.
NOT IN A BOX, NOT WITH A FOX!
......
MEXICO CITY, ESTADIO AZTECA
WOO-HOO—!!
WHOA—!!

WE HAVE THE POWER!
THE FUTURE IS NOW!
OOOHHHHH
KIDS RULE!
KIDS RULE?
WHAT THE HECK ARE THEY SAYING?
I CAN'T CONTROL WHAT THEY QUOTE FROM THE BLOG.

WHAT AM I GONNA SAY?
"MORE POWER TO GROWN-UPS"? I DON'T THINK SO.
HOW MANY READERS DO YOU HAVE NOW?
ABOUT SIX HUNDRED THOUSAND LOG IN PRETTY MUCH EVERY DAY.
OH-HOH?
GRAB
......

FLOAT FLOAT
WOOOOOOT!
TAP...
WOW!

WHEW! IT'S OVER!
YOU'RE NATIONAL HEROES!
I'M STARV-ING.
NOT ONLY HERE...
...BUT IN OTHER COUNTRIES TOO.
YOU GUYS ARE SO YOUNG, BUT YOU'VE ACCOMPLISHED SO MUCH AND EXPOSED SO MUCH EVIL.
PLUS...
...YOU HELPED PUBLICIZE THE MELTING OF THE PLANET'S ICE AND SPOKE TO CONGRESS.

YOU'RE AMAZING.
EXCUSE ME, WHO WORKED UP THE NERVE TO SPEAK TO CONGRESS?
Urg.
WOOOOT!!
NOW WE'RE GOING UP ON-STAGE. ARE YOU READY?
YOU REMEMBER WHAT I SAID YESTERDAY, RIGHT?
YOU GUYS HAVE DONE SO MUCH TO DESERVE THIS AWARD!
CLICK
CLICK
CLICK
CLICK

HA-HA-HA...
I HATE THIS.
GET ME OUTTA HERE.
THIS IS NOT A GOOD SETUP.
BUENOS DÍAS...
...SEÑORS Y SEÑORAS...
WOOOT
HOY NOSOTROS—
AAAAH!

!!

YOU GUYS READY?!
BATTLE UP!

SHOOM!
SMASH!!
SHHP
!!
THEY'RE WEAKER THAN I THOUGHT THEY'D BE.

KICK
GRAB

UGH!
RIP
FWOOOOOH

THUD
CRACK

Y-YUK!
WOBBLE

DASH
SHOOT!

SMASH

WEEE-WOO-I
WEEE-WOO-I

TMP
TMP

WHEW...

MAX, ARE YOU ALL RIGHT?!

YEAH...
AND THE KIDS...?
THEY'RE BEING TREATED OVER THERE.

EEK!
THUD

TMP
DRIP
DRIP
TMP
......
......
OKAY...

...NO MORE AIR SHOWS.

SEEING BATTLES IS HARD...
...IF YOU'RE NOT USED TO IT.
UH-HUH...

......

......

...HMPH.

......
RAGGED
THANKS FOR WORRYING ABOUT ME.

WHAT WERE THOSE THINGS?

NOT SURE.
THEY WEREN'T ERASERS OR ROBOTS...
IT'S A MYSTERY.

HERE WE ARE.

HUH?

CREAK
COME ON IN.
MAX!!

THE CSM ISN'T OUR ONLY CONCERN RIGHT NOW.
WE NEED TO DISCUSS YOUR NEXT STEPS.

OH?

A NEW SCHOOL WAS RECENTLY CREATED—
THE DAY AND NIGHT SCHOOL.

......
YES.

IT'S FOR GIFTED CHILDREN...
...AND IT'S DESIGNED TO LET KIDS LEARN AT THEIR NATURAL PACE, IN WAYS THAT SUIT THEM BEST.

YOU'D ALL DO REALLY WELL THERE.
IT'S ONE OF THE ONLY SCHOOLS ON EARTH WHERE YOU'D FIT IN.

YEAH, WE'RE ALL ABOUT FITTING IN.
WHERE IS IT?

IN A BEAUTIFUL AND SECLUDED PART OF UTAH.
IT'S GOT MOUNTAINS, A LAKE TO SWIM IN...
...AND HORSES TO RIDE.

OOH! I LOVE HORSES!
AND SCHOOL...
TONS OF BOOKS...
...AND OTHER KIDS TO TALK TO...
NUDGE, IT'S OUT OF THE QUESTION.

REALLY? I LIKE SCHOOL.
UM... EVEN THOUGH SOME KIDS ARE BUTTHEADS...
WE USUALLY HAVE BIGGER PROBLEMS THAN KIDS BEING BUTTHEADS.

NUDGE, YOU KNOW WE HAVE TO KEEP ON THE MOVE.
REMEMBER THE SUICIDE-SNIPER GUY?
THERE'S NO WAY WE'D BE SAFE.

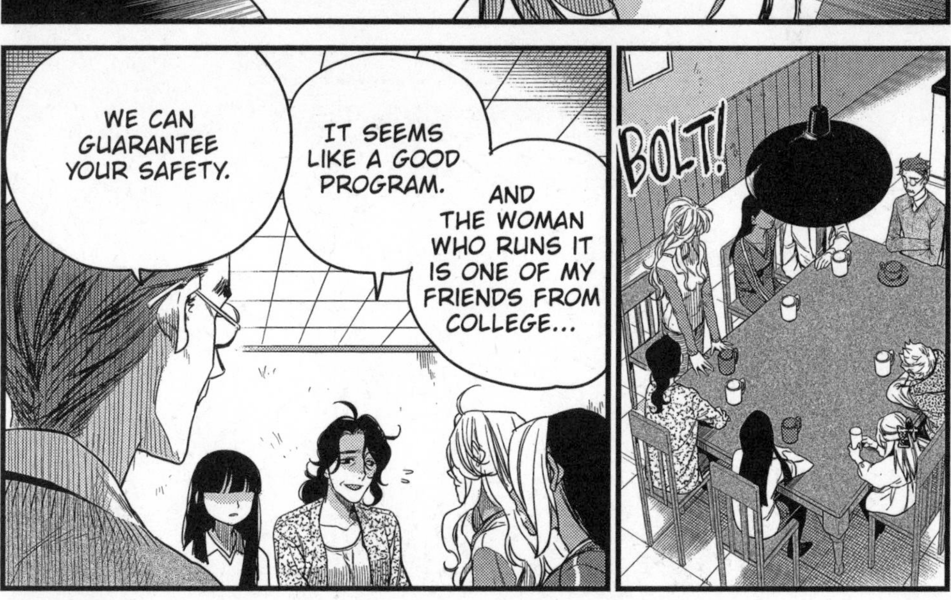
WE CAN GUARANTEE YOUR SAFETY.
IT SEEMS LIKE A GOOD PROGRAM.
AND THE WOMAN WHO RUNS IT IS ONE OF MY FRIENDS FROM COLLEGE...
BOLT!

TMP
TMP
SCHOOL IS OUT.

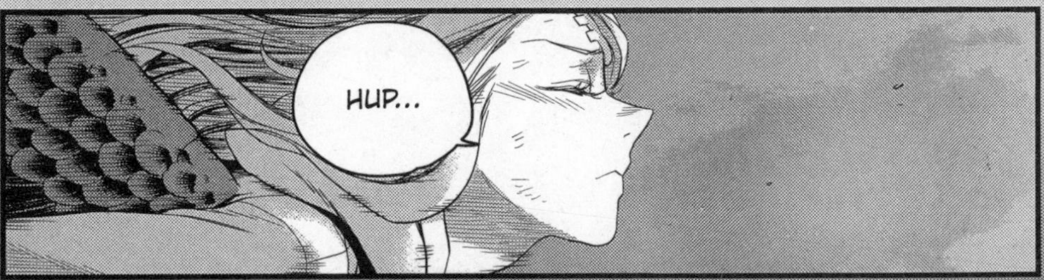

WHY DOES THE REST OF THE FLOCK KEEP PRETENDING THAT WE HAVE CHOICES?

IT'S A WASTE OF TIME.

WORSE, IT'S ALWAYS UP TO ME TO BE THE BAD GUY...

...THE ONE WHO SHOOTS DOWN EVERYONE'S HOPES AND DREAMS.
YOU THINK I LIKE BEING THE HEAVY?
I DON'T.

AND FANG. HE USUALLY SUPPORTS ME.
WHICH I APPRECIATE.
BUT LATELY HE'S BEEN LOBBYING FOR US TO FIND A DESERTED ISLAND SOMEWHERE AND JUST KICK BACK, EAT COCONUTS, AND CHILL...
...WITHOUT ANYONE KNOWING WHERE WE ARE.
SOMETIMES THAT SOUNDS REALLY GOOD.

BUT HOW LONG CAN THAT LAST?

SOONER OR LATER, NUDGE IS GOING TO WANT NEW SHOES...

...OR GAZZY WILL RUN OUT OF COMIC BOOKS, OR ANGEL WILL DECIDE SHE WANTS TO RULE THE WORLD...

...AND THEN WHERE WOULD WE BE?

RIGHT.

WE'D BE BACK TO ME TELLING EVERYONE NO.

WHUK
ACK!

MAXIMUM RIDE

MAXIMUM RIDE
CHAPTER 55

I TOLD YOU SHE WAS NOT TO BE KILLED!

IT IS NOT DEAD...

IT IS... LIMP.

SHE'S BLOODY.

SSK...

WE SHOT IT TO GET IT OUT OF THE SKY.
HACK COUGH
WOBBLE...
MAXIMUM RIDE.
I AM MR. CHU.

WHAT DO YOU WANT...
...MR. CHU?
THIS SUBTLE SHIFTING... WE MUST BE ON A BOAT.
I WANT TO EXPLAIN TO YOU...
...THAT YOU MUST IMMEDIATELY SEVER YOUR TIES...
...TO THE COALITION TO STOP THE MADNESS.
AND?
YOU DO NOT KNOW WHAT THEY ARE REALLY UP TO.
THEY ARE JUST USING YOU TO PROMOTE THEIR OWN AGENDA.
THEY'RE PAYING US IN DONUTS.
THROB

I REPRESENT A GROUP OF VERY POWERFUL, VERY WEALTHY BUSINESSMEN FROM AROUND THE WORLD.
SSK

OF COURSE YOU DO.
EXIT, EXIT, EXIT.
GLANCE
WE ARE THE ONLY ONES WHO REALLY KNOW WHAT IS GOING ON.
A SKY-LIGHT!

COULD I— OH.
MAX NO FLY. BUMMER.

THERE IS AN APOCALYPSE COMING.

YOU'RE NOT THE FIRST PERSON WHO'S TOLD ME THAT.
IT IS TRUE!
MY GROUP WILL SURVIVE THE APOCALYPSE.

WE ARE THE ONLY ONES WHO WILL NOT BECOME EXTINCT...
...AFTER THE WORLD LEADERS SUCCEED IN THEIR QUEST TO DESTROY ONE ANOTHER.
KINDA MAKES YOU WISH YOU WERE A WORLD LEADER YOURSELF...
...HUH?
SMIRK
SLAP

YOU STUPID, ARROGANT GIRL.
ROAR!!
IF YOU AND YOUR FLOCK WILL JOIN OUR GROUP...
...THEN YOU WILL NOT BE HUNTED DOWN AND DESTROYED.
PTEW.
WE CAN USE YOU ON OUR TEAM.
TMP
BUT IF YOU KEEP UP WITH THE WISECRACKS AND YOUR STUPIDITY...
...YOU WILL SOON BE ELIMINATED.
THERE WILL BE NO ROOM FOR YOU IN THE NEW WORLD.

AGAIN, NOT NEW INFORMATION.
THE FLOCK AND I AREN'T FOR SALE...
...CHUEY.

SO ALL I CAN SAY IS...
CLENCH!
...BRING IT!
WHOOSH

TCH.
MY LEFT EYE...
I CAN'T TELL THE DISTANCE...

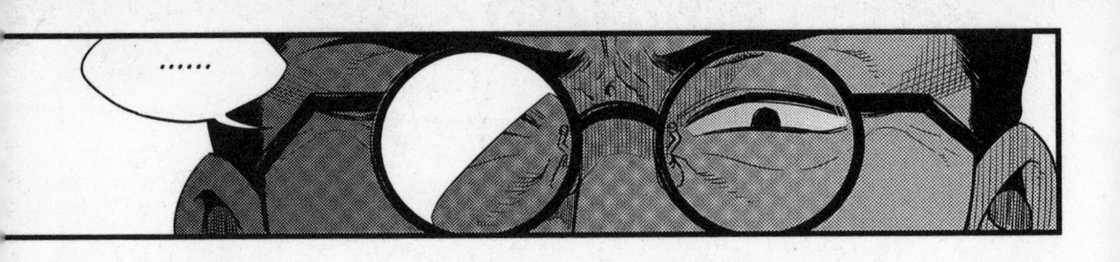
......

I AM SORRY THAT YOU AND THE FLOCK WILL BE DEAD SOON.

TMP
TMP
BUT MY SCIENTISTS WILL ENJOY TAKING YOU APART...
...TO FIND OUT WHAT MAKES YOU TICK.
IF YOUR SCIENTISTS TAKE ME APART...
HMPH!

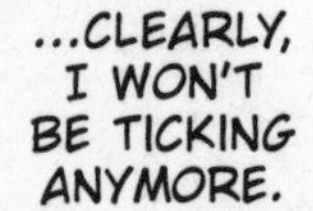
...CLEARLY, I WON'T BE TICKING ANYMORE.

URK!

TURN
YOU MAY THINK I AM DREAMING...
...BUT I AM NOT.
WHAT I SAY IS TRUE.

IT IS AS REAL AS THE PAIN IN YOUR WING AND ON YOUR FACE.
AND SPEAKING OF PAIN...
...MAXIMUM...
...YOU SHOULD KNOW THAT WE ARE EXPERTS IN THE ART OF PERSUASION.

PAIN FADES...
SMIRK

...BUT BEING A NUTCASE SEEMS TO STICK AROUND.
GRIND
GUESS WHO GOT THE BETTER DEAL HERE?

TOSS——..

VROOOM—

OWWW...
UGH... THROWING ME OUT OF A MOVING CAR...
THEY'VE BEEN WATCHING TOO MANY MOVIES...

MAN, I'M HUNGRY...
SLUMP
SLUMP
SLUMP

OH—

IF I GO IN LIKE THIS...
RAGGED
...THEY'RE GOING TO BE SHOCKED, HUH...?
RAGGED

WHAT...WHAT HAPPENED?!
UHH...YOU KNOW...I WAS FLYING...
MUMBLE
...AND THERE WAS, LIKE, A STRAY BULLET... A FREAK ACCIDENT, REALLY...
MUMBLE

COME IN AND SIT.
JEB, WOULD YOU PLEASE GET THE FIRST AID KIT FROM MY TRUNK?
ALL RIGHT.

THERE, YOU'RE ALL PATCHED UP NOW.

THANKS.
IT'S A GOOD THING MOM'S A VET...

YOU SHOULDN'T FLY FOR AT LEAST A WEEK.

SO, THREE DAYS...

AND I REALLY MEAN A WEEK!
NOT THREE DAYS!

AH— THE AIR'S GREAT.
YUCATÁN
IT REALLY IS BEAUTIFUL HERE.

BUT WHAT DOES THE AIR QUALITY MATTER ANYWAY? I STILL CAN'T FLY.

JEB.

HAVE YOU EVER HEARD OF A MR. CHU?
......

NO...
...CAN'T SAY THAT I HAVE. WHERE DID YOU HEAR THAT NAME?

HMM.

WA-HA-HA!
TMP
TMP
SHUDDER

MAX...
COME ON.
I'M GOING TO SHOW YOU HOW TO MAKE PUCHERO YUCATECO.

HUH—
WHY IS MAX IN THE KITCHEN?

WE'RE COOKING.
SHE'S JUST KEEPING YOU COMPANY...
...RIGHT?

NO.
SHE'S COOKING.
BOIL
BOIL

WHISPER
WHISPER
Cooking... food?
Maybe we should order a pizza?
GRRRR!!

YES, I'M COOKING FOOD, AND IT'S GREAT!
AND YOU'RE GOING TO EAT IT, YOU TWERPS!
HA-HA-HA
URK!
Eat it!
ACK!
EEK!!
HA-HA-HA
It's actually not bad!
HA-HA
AND THAT'S HOW I SPENT MY THREE DAYS OF FORCED REST.
THE FLOCK SAW ALL THE MAYAN WONDERS OF THE YUCATÁN...
...AND I LEARNED HOW TO COOK SOMETHING BESIDES COLD CEREAL.
SO THERE WAS MUCH AMAZEMENT ALL AROUND.

THEY WANTED TO TRY JEB'S DAY AND NIGHT SCHOOL.

WOW! IT'S HUGE!!
SCHOOL!
SCHOOL, SCHOOL!
A SCHOOL IN THE DESERT...

MAX.
?
PLEASE DON'T IMPART ANY PEARLS OF WISDOM.
I JUST ATE.
SHAKE SHAKE
JUST—
BEWARE OF MR. CHU.
HE MAKES ITEX LOOK LIKE SESAME STREET.
MM.
HELLO.

I'M MS. HAMILTON.
MAX...
...IT'S GOOD TO FINALLY MEET YOU.
YOUR MOM AND I WENT TO COLLEGE TOGETHER.
WELCOME TO THE DAY AND NIGHT SCHOOL.
I HOPE YOU'LL BE HAPPY HERE.

FIRST, WE NEED TO TEST YOUR KNOWLEDGE.

SO WE'LL KNOW YOUR STRENGTHS AND WEAKNESSES.
THEN WE'LL KNOW WHAT CLASSES WILL BE BEST FOR YOU.

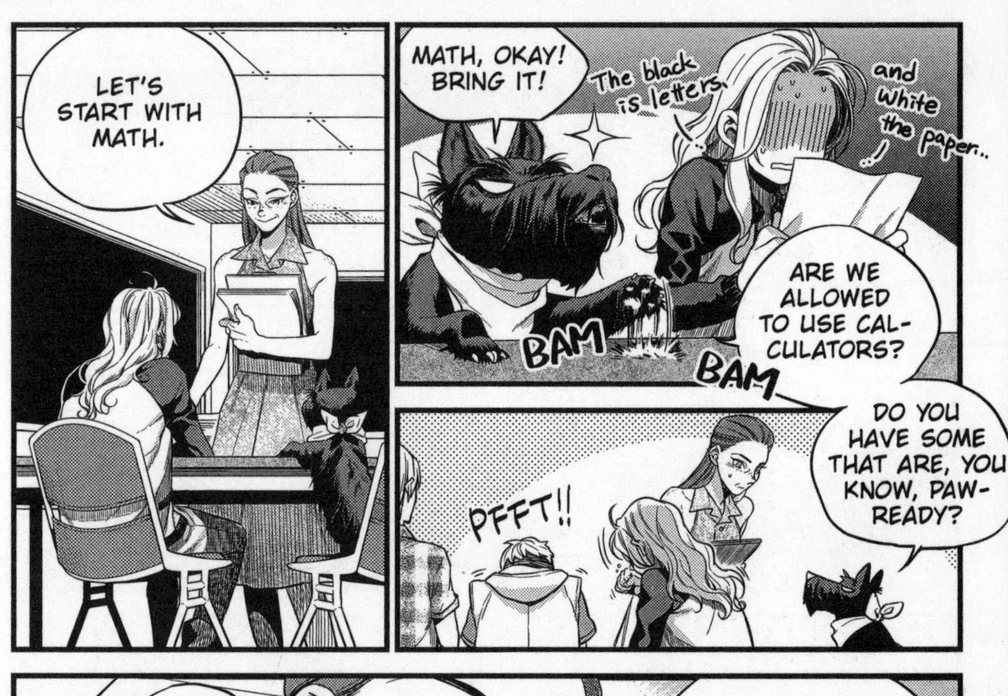
LET'S START WITH MATH.
MATH, OKAY! BRING IT!
The black is letters...
and white the paper...
BAM
BAM
ARE WE ALLOWED TO USE CALCULATORS?
DO YOU HAVE SOME THAT ARE, YOU KNOW, PAW-READY?
PFFT!!

NO.
WE DON'T HAVE ANY PAW-READY CALCULATORS.

BUT YOU PROBABLY WON'T NEED ONE FOR THESE QUESTIONS ANYWAY.
FLAP
HMM...

IN SHORT...
...YOU'RE VERY, VERY, VERY BRIGHT KIDS...
...WHO HAVEN'T HAD MUCH SCHOOLING.

I COULD HAVE TOLD YOU THAT.
AND YOU DON'T EVEN KNOW ABOUT THE OTHER STUFF WE CAN DO...
...LIKE HACKING COMPUTERS AND JACKING CARS AND BREAKING INTO MOST BUILDINGS.
ANGEL, YOU'RE SO FAR OFF THE CHART...
...THAT WE'LL HAVE TO INVENT A SPECIAL CHART JUST FOR YOU.
I THOUGHT YOU MIGHT.

I'VE BEEN HERE FOR FIVE HOURS...
...AND SO FAR I HAVEN'T REALLY WANTED TO TAKE ANYONE APART. WEIRD.
BUT THAT DOESN'T MEAN I WANT TO STAY AT THE DAY AND NIGHT SCHOOL.

SOUTH AMERICA.
IT'LL BE WARM. THEY HAVE LLAMAS.
YOU LIKE LLAMAS.
HOW LONG DO YOU THINK IT WILL TAKE ANOTHER SUICIDE SNIPER TO FIND US?
I WANT TO STAY HERE.
THIS PLACE IS OUT IN THE DESERT.
SHRUG

AND MS. HAMILTON TOLD US ABOUT ALL THE SAFETY MEASURES—
THE ALARMS, THE LIGHTS, THE RADAR.
THIS IS WHAT WE'VE BEEN LOOKING FOR.

I'M TIRED OF BEING SCARED, MAX.

WE ALL ARE!
AND AS SOON AS WE FINISH OUR BIG MISSION, WE'LL BE ABLE TO RELAX.
I PROMISE!

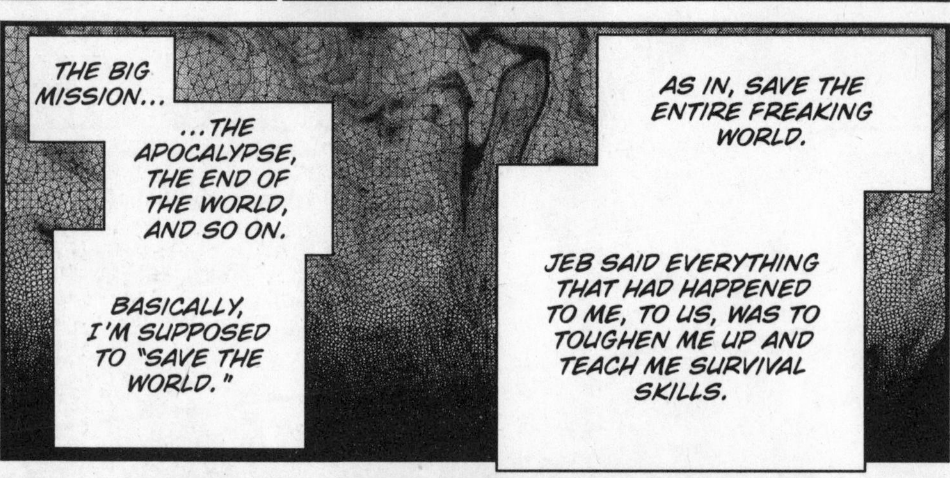
THE BIG MISSION...
...THE APOCALYPSE, THE END OF THE WORLD, AND SO ON.
BASICALLY, I'M SUPPOSED TO "SAVE THE WORLD."
AS IN, SAVE THE ENTIRE FREAKING WORLD.
JEB SAID EVERYTHING THAT HAD HAPPENED TO ME, TO US, WAS TO TOUGHEN ME UP AND TEACH ME SURVIVAL SKILLS.

I JUST WANT TO FIT IN.
I WANT TO BE LIKE OTHER KIDS.

NUDGE...
...MOST OF THE OTHER KIDS HERE SEEM LIKE SPINELESS, GULLIBLE WEENIES WHO WOULDN'T SURVIVE ONE DAY ON THEIR OWN.
THAT'S THE POINT!
THEY DON'T NEED TO!
THEY'RE NOT ON THEIR OWN—
PEOPLE TAKE CARE OF THEM.
I'VE...
...ALWAYS TAKEN CARE OF YOU AND THE OTHERS AS BEST I COULD.
......
BUT YOU'RE JUST A KID YOURSELF.

I WANT TO BE NORMAL.

I WANT TO BE LIKE OTHER KIDS.

I'M TIRED OF BEING A FREAK...

...AND HAVING TO RUN ALL THE TIME AND NEVER BEING ABLE TO SETTLE DOWN.

I WANT A HOME.
AND I KNOW HOW TO GET ONE.
HOW?

...HAVE WINGS.
MUMBLE...

WHAT?
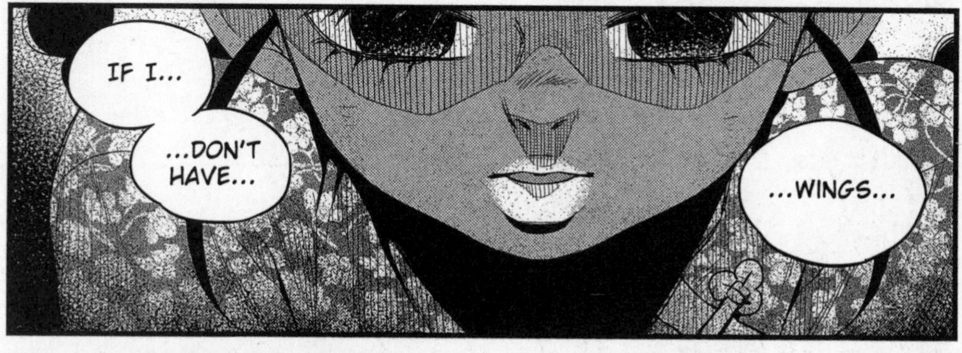
IF I...
...DON'T HAVE...
...WINGS...

...TAKE THEM OFF.
CLENCH
NUDGE, YOU **COME** WITH WINGS.
YOU'RE THE WINGED VERSION. THERE'S NO OPTIONAL NUDGE WITH NO WINGS.

HIC...
HIC...
HIC...

NUDGE...
HUG
HIC...
HIC...
...GETTING YOUR WINGS TAKEN OFF WON'T MAKE YOU NOT A BIRD KID.
BEING IN THE FLOCK IS MORE THAN JUST ABOUT HAVING WINGS.

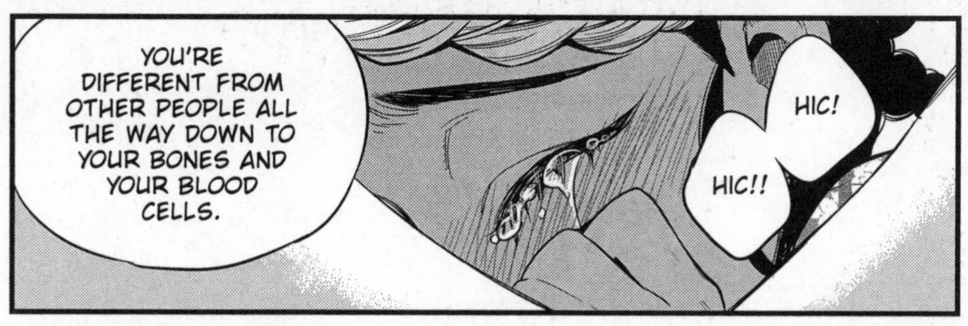
YOU'RE DIFFERENT FROM OTHER PEOPLE ALL THE WAY DOWN TO YOUR BONES AND YOUR BLOOD CELLS.
HIC!
HIC!!

WHAT I MEAN IS, YOU'RE SPECIAL, EVERY BIT OF YOU.
MORE SPECIAL THAN ANY OTHER KID IN THE WHOLE WORLD...
...INCLUDING THE ONES YOU WANT TO BE LIKE.

YOU'RE BEAUTIFUL AND POWERFUL...
...AND UNIQUE.
KIDS WITHOUT WINGS DON'T HAVE YOUR STRENGTH, YOUR SMARTS, YOUR DETERMINATION.

SHAKE
SHAKE
THERE'S A DIFFERENCE BETWEEN BEING SPECIAL...
...AND BEING A TOTAL FREAK.
I'M A TOTAL FREAK.
AND I'M STAYING HERE.

MAXIMUM

RIDE

...THEN SHE SAID THAT SHE'S A TOTAL FREAK...
...AND THAT SHE'S STAYING HERE.
SHE'S CONFUSED.
SHE'S JUST A KID.

YOU KNOW WE HAVE TO GO.
WHAT IF SHE REALLY WON'T COME WITH US?

HOW CAN WE FORCE HER?

WE...

EVEN IF WE MADE HER COME...
...SHE'D JUST HOLD IT AGAINST US. SHE'D BE MAD.

YOU HAVE TO WANT TO BE WITH SOMEONE, OR IT DOESN'T WORK.
WHOOSH
YOU HAVE TO CHOOSE.

UH...
YEAH...

UM, AND SHE...

SSK
I CHOOSE *YOU*...
...MAX.

MAXIMUM
RIDE
CHAPTER 56

WE HAD KISSED A COUPLE OF TIMES BEFORE...
...BUT THIS WAS DIFFERENT.
WHAT STARTED OUT SO PASSIONATE GRADUALLY BECAME LESS HUNGRY AND MORE COMFORTING.
AND THEN I STARTED MY INEVITABLE HYSTERICAL FREAK-OUT, BUT I TRIED TO DO IT VERY QUIETLY INSIDE MY HEAD...
...BECAUSE THIS HAD BEEN SO SPECIAL...
...AND I DIDN'T WANT TO RUIN IT. LIKE I USUALLY DID.
I WANTED TO STAY IN THE MOMENT FEELING VULNERABLE...
...AND THINK ABOUT EVERYTHING THAT HAD JUST HAPPENED BETWEEN US...

...AND WONDER HOW IT HAD CHANGED THINGS...

...AND WONDER WHEN I HAD STARTED...
BA-DUMP
...TO LOVE HIM SO MUCH...
...AND FEEL HOW TERRIFIED I WAS AND HOW ELATED...
BA-DUMP
...AND HOW EVERY CELL OF MY BODY FELT SO ALIVE.
BA-DUMP

MAX! FANG!!
WHY ARE ALL THE LIGHTS ON?
THIS CAN'T BE A GOOD SIGN.
TAP
SKID

WHAT'S GOING ON?
WHY'S EVERYONE UP?
NO, NO, SWEETIE. JUST A LITTLE NIGHTTIME SPIN.

TEARY TEARY
I THOUGHT YOU WERE GONE!
I THOUGHT THEY HAD GOTTEN YOU!

IT'S, UH...

WHAT?!
IT'S YOUR MOM, MAX...
SHE'S BEEN KIDNAPPED.
SHE'S GONE.

...PHONE CALL.
ELLA CALLED.

SHE'S HYSTERICAL— YOUR MOM DISAPPEARED FROM THE AIRPORT THIS AFTERNOON WHILE THEY WERE BETWEEN FLIGHTS.
DR. MARTINEZ JUST WENT TO THE RESTROOM AND NEVER CAME BACK.
RIGHT NOW ELLA'S AT HER AUNT'S HOUSE. I DON'T THINK JEB KNOWS.

ELLA WAS GOING TO CALL HIM AFTER SHE TALKED TO US.
DID THEY CALL THE POLICE OR THE FBI?

WE DON'T KNOW...

RIIIIING

CLICK
Max?
It's Dr. John Abate from the CSM.
Are you all okay?
YES...
WHAT'S GOING ON?
A fax just came in to the CSM office that Valencia has been kidnapped...
YEAH, ELLA CALLED.
WHO WAS THE FAX FROM?
It looks like the origination number got cut off...
... somehow during transmis-sion.
We don't know.
CLICK
CLICK
ROLLL

But it says that Valencia has been kidnapped ...
...and will be held until the CSM quits its efforts...
...to put pressure on big businesses.

UH-HUH.
ANY-THING ELSE?

Just a minute ago, we received another fax.
BEEP
CLICK
It's a photo showing Valencia held hostage, alive, but we don't know how long ago that was.
The weird thing is, it looks like she's being held on a boat.
A BOAT?

We've called the FBI, of course. They'll probably want to talk to you too.
You were among the last people to see her.
I want you guys to sit tight for a couple hours, okay?
Let me get some answers before you go charging off.
I DO NOT "GO CHARGING OFF"!
YOUR MIDDLE NAME IS "CHARGING OFF."
We're going to try to figure out if we can tell where the boat is by the picture.
I'll call you as soon as I can. Stay by the phone.
OKAY.
IN OTHER NEWS...
HUH?

THE HOUSE IS SURROUNDED.

IT LOOKS
LIKE THOSE
THINGS FROM
MEXICO CITY.

CLENCH
DAMN...
SHUDDER
DR. ABATE SAID TO SIT TIGHT.
DR. ABATE DIDN'T KNOW ABOUT THE COMBAT ROBOTS SENT TO KILL US.

OH, GOSH, I GUESS THEY WON'T, THEN.
THEY HAVEN'T ATTACKED YET.

ANYWAY, HOW MANY OF THEM ARE THERE?
LOOKS LIKE, ABOUT... EIGHTY?
MAX...
ZZZZT
...HIH-MUM...
...RIDE.

PEEK
THESE GUYS HAVE... IT LOOKS LIKE UZIS ATTACHED TO THEIR ARMS.
UZIS. THE AUTOMATIC ONES.
HM...

EVERYONE, GET UPSTAIRS TO THE HALL, WHERE THERE AREN'T ANY WINDOWS.
STAY DOWN, BUT BE READY TO DO AN UP-AND-AWAY IF YOU HEAR A BUNCH OF BREAKING GLASS.

ZZZT
MAX-HIH-MUM RIDE...
ZZT
SHOULD I ANSWER HIM?
......

I THINK YOU SHOULD LOOK AT HIM.
?

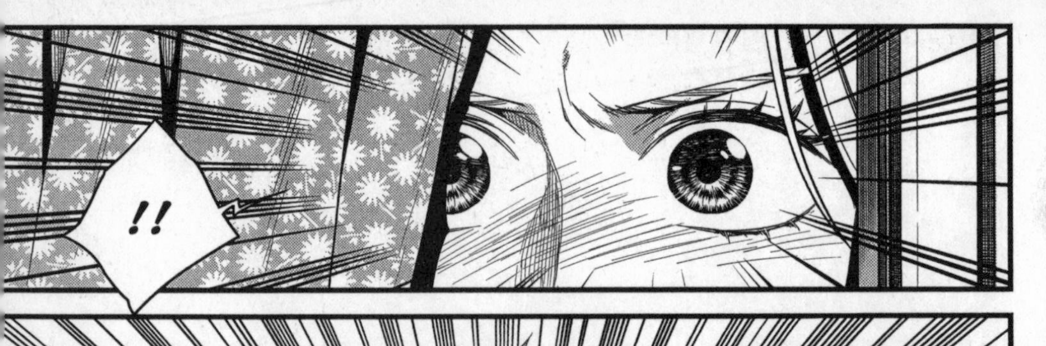
!!

ARI?!

BUT HE'S... DEAD.
SSK...
THEY JUST MADE IT LOOK LIKE THAT TO FREAK YOU OUT.
THEY SUCCEEDED.
HA!
WHAT DO THEY WANT?

THEY WANT ME—US—TO QUIT WORKING FOR THE CSM.
REMEMBER WHEN I CAME BACK WITH MY NEW, VENTILATED WING?
THEY DID IT—THEY TOOK ME TO A GUY CALLED MR. CHU.
SHORT, I THINK HE'S CHINESE, MAJOR BEE UP HIS BUTT.

HE TOLD ME HE'D FIND A WAY TO MAKE ME STOP WORKING FOR THE CSM.
HE SAID HE REPRESENTED A BUNCH OF SUPER-POWERFUL BUSINESSMEN.

AND YOU DIDN'T TELL ANYONE BECAUSE...?
I...WANTED TO DO SOME RESEARCH.
LATER I MENTIONED IT TO THE JEBSTER...
...AND HE WENT PALE.
MAX-HIH-MUM RIDE.
HOW HARD WOULD IT BE TO PROGRAM HIM TO SAY MY NAME CORRECTLY?
YOU MUST NOT LEAVE THE AREA.

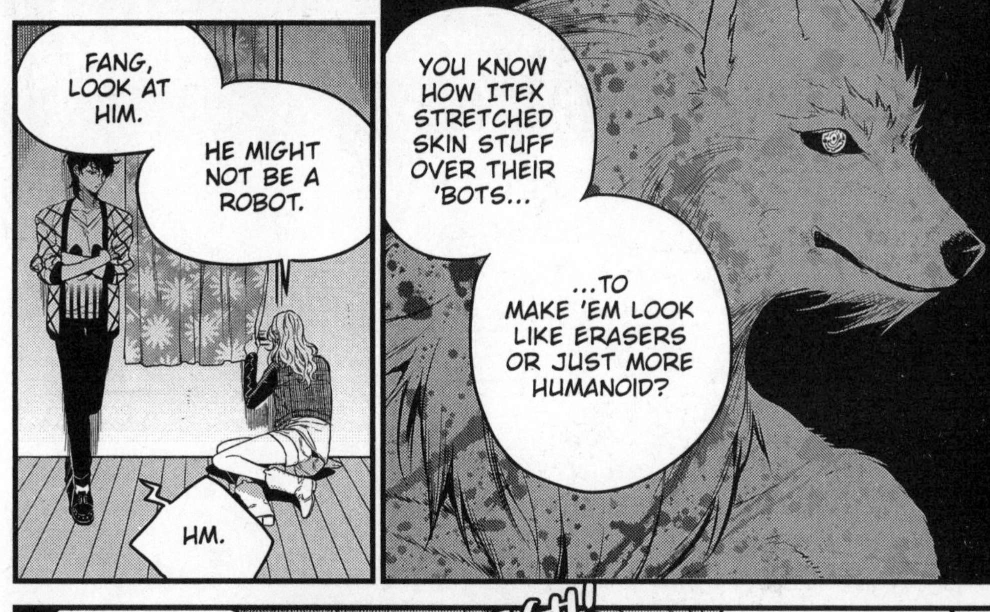
FANG, LOOK AT HIM.
HE MIGHT NOT BE A ROBOT.
HM.
YOU KNOW HOW ITEX STRETCHED SKIN STUFF OVER THEIR 'BOTS...
...TO MAKE 'EM LOOK LIKE ERASERS OR JUST MORE HUMANOID?

THIS GUY— IT'S LIKE THEY TOOK A PERSON AND THEN BUILT A ROBOT INSIDE OF HIM.
BLEGH!
GOING FROM THE INSIDE OUT INSTEAD OF THE OUTSIDE IN, YOU KNOW? GROSS.

......
IS IT HARD, BEING YOU?
YES, IT *IS*, ACTUALLY.
BUT ARE YOU SAYING THAT NO ONE COULD POSSIBLY BE TWISTED ENOUGH TO TAKE A PERSON AND THEN GROW A CYBORG INSIDE OF IT?

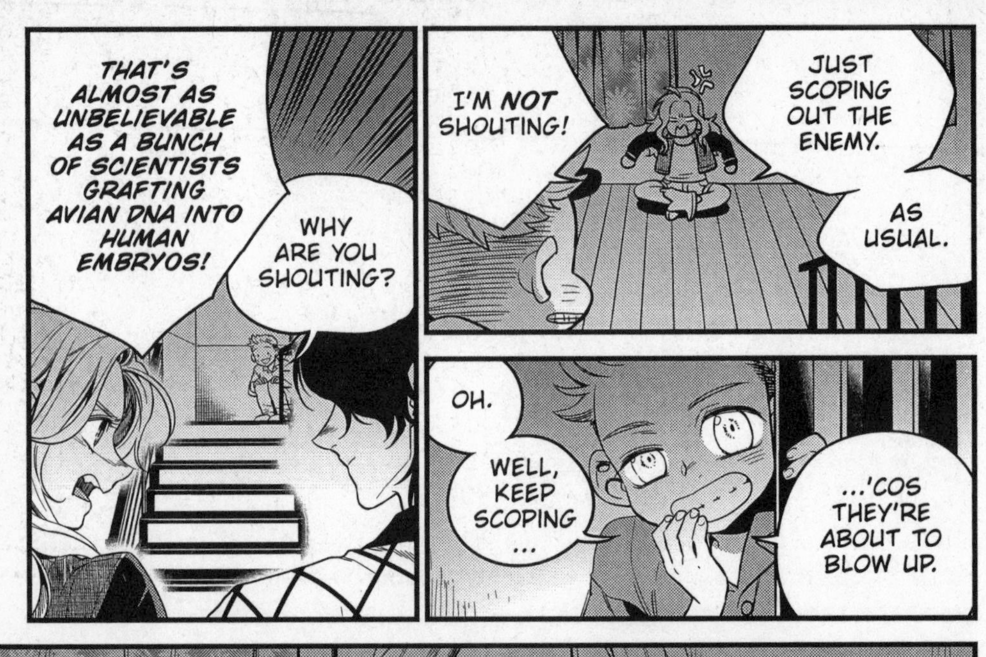
THAT'S ALMOST AS UNBELIEVABLE AS A BUNCH OF SCIENTISTS GRAFTING AVIAN DNA INTO HUMAN EMBRYOS!
WHY ARE YOU SHOUTING?
I'M NOT SHOUTING!
JUST SCOPING OUT THE ENEMY.
AS USUAL.
OH.
WELL, KEEP SCOPING ...
...'COS THEY'RE ABOUT TO BLOW UP.

BLOW UP?
THUNDER ...?!
CRAWL
OKAY, HERE IT COMES!
GOD IN HEAVEN. HE CAN'T MANIPULATE THE WEATHER NOW, CAN HE?
CRAWL

RATTLE
RATTLE
PZZT
PZZT
...SILENCE...

KRA THOOM
PZZZZZZZT

AAAACK!!
RATTLE
RATTLE
SILENCE...
HUH?

?
?
SSK
CLATTER!
OH, WAY, WAY AWESOME, DUDE!
THIS WAS THE PINNACLE OF OUR PYROMANIA!

EXCITED!!
NEXT THING YOU KNOW, THEY'RE EXTRA CRISPY!
WE SAW BIG THUNDERHEADS FORMING IN THE DISTANCE—THE FIRST TIME IN YEARS, I BET!
AND THE BEST PART? THEY WERE STANDING SO CLOSE TOGETHER THAT THEY HELPED FRY EACH OTHER!
THIS HOUSE HAD A LIGHTNING ROD ON THE ROOF! WE DISCONNECTED IT, AIMED IT AT THE DUMB-BOTS, AND ENHANCED ITS POWERS A TAD!

PZZZT
PZZZT
WOW...
THEY'RE FRIED ALL RIGHT.
I'M BRILLIANT! I'M A GENIUS!
I CAN BLOW UP THE WORLD!

SEE IF THERE ARE ANY SALVAGEABLE WEAPONS.

AH— HOT, HOT—
MAX-PZZT...

MAX-HIH-PZZT...
......
IT'S NOT ARI...

SO...
...HOW'S MR. CHU, THAT SCAMP?

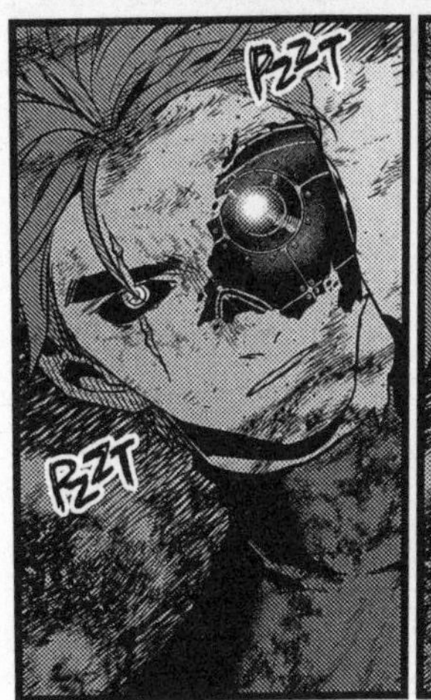
PZZT
PZZT

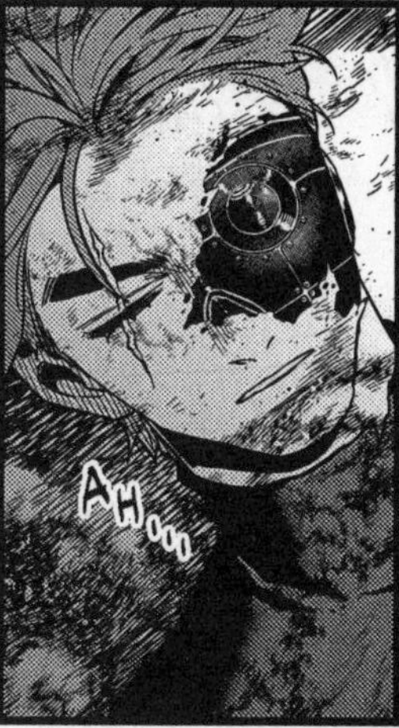
AH...

......

RIIIING
PACK LIGHT.
WE'RE MOVING OUT.

REGULAR CORDED PHONE.
NOT CONNECTED TO THE ELECTRICAL SYSTEM.
?

CLICK
We've got some details about Valencia's disappearance...
PHEW
Max— good, you're there.
WHAT?

To be on the safe side, we're sending a car for you. It should be there in about an hour.
UM, NOT SO MUCH ANYMORE.
...but I don't want to discuss them on the phone.
We've been tipped that your house might be under surveillance.

IT'LL BE DAWN THEN.

BETTER MAKE IT AN ARMORED ONE.

CLICK...

......

KNOCK KNOCK
SSK
HI.

THEY GOT THE WORST OF IT, HUH?
ALWAYS DO.
DOESN'T LOOK LIKE YOU'RE HURT ANYWHERE.
WHAT A RELIEF, FANG.
LET'S HURRY. WE'VE GOT A PLANE WAITING.
......
FLINCH

ON THE WAY, YOU CAN FILL ME IN ON WHAT HAPPENED.
AND VICE VERSA.
TMP
TMP
RIGHT.
SSK
MAX.

......
GULP...

I'M...

...STAYING.

YOU CAN'T. IT'S NOT SAFE.
I CAN'T DO THIS ANYMORE.
I'LL BE SAFE AT THE SCHOOL, IN THE DORMS.
I WANT TO GO TO SCHOOL.
I JUST WANT TO BE A KID.
AT LEAST FOR A WHILE.

I HAD A MILLION EXCELLENT ARGUMENTS WHY SHE'S WRONG AND MAKING THE BIGGEST MISTAKE OF HER LIFE, BUT WHEN I OPENED MY MOUTH TO GET STARTED, IT HIT ME—

IT'S POINTLESS.

NUDGE ISN'T FOUR OR FIVE. SHE'S AROUND ELEVEN AND WILL BE AS TALL AS ME IN ANOTHER YEAR OR SO.

WHAT SHE REALLY MEANT WAS THAT SHE **COULDN'T** DO THIS ANYMORE.

CLENCH

IF SHE DOESN'T WANT TO BE WITH US...

...DOESN'T WANT TO FIGHT...

...SHE'LL GET HURT—BAD.

YOU...

...MAY **NOT** GET YOUR WINGS TAKEN OFF.
......?

YOU MAY GET YOUR EARS PIERCED.
OR YOUR NOSE. OR— ACTUALLY, NOTHING ELSE.
AND YOU ABSOLUTELY, POSITIVELY, MAY NEVER, ***EVER*** GET YOUR WINGS REMOVED.
MAX...

OR I SWEAR TO GOD, I WILL COME BACK...
...AND KICK YOUR SKINNY, FASHION-CONSCIOUS BUTT INTO NEXT WEEK. DO YOU HEAR ME?
YES!
YES, YES! THANK YOU, THANK YOU, THANK YOU!
I LOVE YOU SO MUCH!

WE'RE TAKING THIS MILITARY JET TO SAN DIEGO.
......
NUDGE...
GRAB
IT'LL BE OKAY, MAX.
EVERY-THING.

MAXIMUM RIDE
CHAPTER 57
EVERY-THING WILL BE OKAY.

MURMUR
MURMUR
"CLICK"
THANK YOU FOR JOINING US, COMMANDER.
WHY ARE THESE CHILDREN HERE?
4:00 PM
THEY ARE INTEGRAL TO OUR INVESTIGATION.
FOR ONE THING, THIS CHILD, MAX, IS DR. MARTINEZ'S DAUGHTER.

ALL THE MORE REASON THIS CONFERENCE IS INAPPROPRIATE FOR CHILDREN.
SEND THEM OUT.
THESE CHILDREN ARE DIFFERENT.
EXCUSE ME.
SSK
YOU THINK YOU COULD SCROUNGE UP SOME PICO DE GALLO?

?!

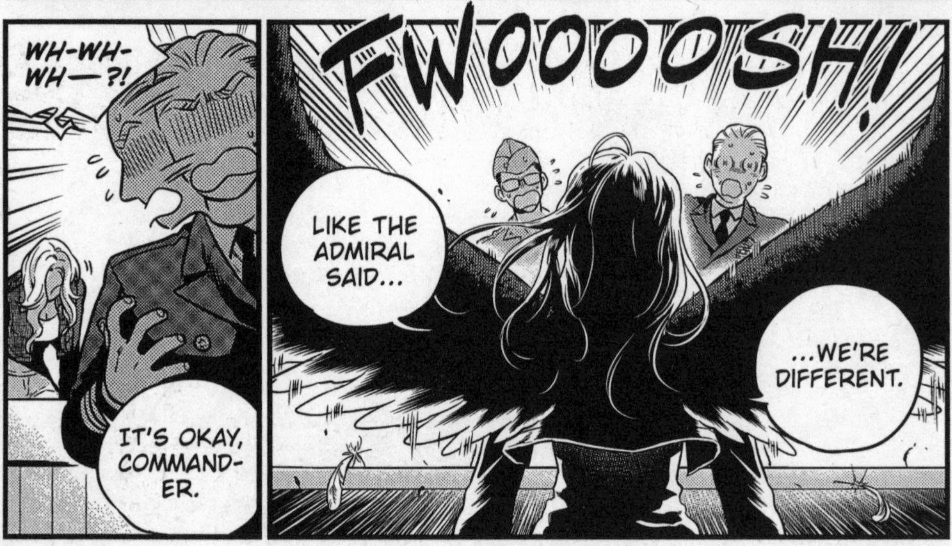
WH-WH-WH—?!
IT'S OKAY, COMMAND-ER.
FWOOOOOSH!
LIKE THE ADMIRAL SAID...
...WE'RE DIFFERENT.

SO HOW 'BOUT WE JUST GET ON WITH THE SHOW, EH?
WE'RE TALKING ABOUT MY MOM HERE.

FLICK!!
The birds are working.

"THE BIRDS ARE WORKING." WHAT THE HECK DOES THAT MEAN?
AND WHAT DOES IT HAVE TO DO WITH MY MOM?

THIS WAS FILMED YESTERDAY EVENING AT NINETEEN-HUNDRED HOURS, AT TWENTY-ONE DEGREES...
CLICK
...THIRTY MINUTES NORTH, ONE HUNDRED FIFTY-SEVEN DEGREES, FORTY MINUTES WEST...

...IN THE PACIFIC OCEAN, OFF THE COAST OF HAWAII.
CLICK

SEABIRDS?
WHAT ARE THEY DOING?
IT'S LIKE, FREE-SHRIMP DAY OR SOMETHING!

WE DON'T KNOW.
CLICK
BUT WAIT.
NANIMOKU

NANI-MOKU?
NANIMOKU
SOMETHING FROM BENEATH THE WATER SMASHED UP THE FISHING BOAT.
MURMUR MURMUR
WAS THAT A WHALE, COMMAND-ER?
UNKNOWN. IT COULD HAVE BEEN A WHALE OR A SUBMARINE.

WE'VE GONE OVER THIS FOOTAGE A HUNDRED TIMES WITH NO SUCCESS.
CLICK
BUT NOW, LOOK AT THIS.
SHUDDER

NAN

ZOOM IN THIS PART.

......
......

M-MOM...

NAN
WE BELIEVE THIS PICTURE WAS TAKEN ON A SUBMARINE.
!!
WE THINK THE SUBMARINE WAS IN THE AREA AND PROBABLY CAPSIZED THAT BOAT.
...WE BELIEVE THAT DR. MARTINEZ IS SOMEWHERE AROUND THERE.
THEY MUST BE HOLDING DR. MARTINEZ UNDER WATER.
AND SINCE WE KNOW THAT BOAT WAS CAPSIZED IN THE PACIFIC OCEAN, OFF THE COAST OF HAWAII...
WHAT DOES "THE BIRDS ARE WORKING" MEAN?
THERE WAS AN AUDIO CLIP WITH THE BIRD FILM...
...AND WHEN WE SPED UP THE SOUND BY FIVE HUNDRED PERCENT, THAT WAS THE PHRASE WE HEARD.
BOLT
MAX, SIT DOWN.
......
WE HAVE A PLAN.
WE NEED YOUR HELP.

WOOOOSH
ARE WE PLANNING TO DIVE-BOMB THE SUBMARINE?
IS THIS PLANE EQUIPPED WITH MARINE MISSILES?
HAHA
NO.
IT'S TAKING US TO ANOTHER U.S. NAVY BASE...
...IN HAWAII.
THE NAVY HAS AGREED TO HELP US GET VALENCIA BACK.
HAS THE CSM AGREED TO BACK OFF BIG COMPANIES?
NO. WE'VE BEEN IN DISCUSSIONS.
WE FEEL THAT VALENCIA WOULD NEVER FORGIVE US IF SHE FOUND OUT THEY HAD MADE US CAVE.
SLUMP
...YOU'RE PROBABLY RIGHT.

JOHN?
YES?

WHAT WOULD HAPPEN IF A BIG BIRD, LIKE A GOOSE, FLEW INTO THE JET ENGINE?
IT WOULD PROBABLY BE VERY BAD.

WHAT WOULD HAPPEN IF SOMEONE HUMMED A FOOTBALL INTO THE ENGINE, RIGHT WHEN THE PLANE WAS TAKING OFF?
IS THERE A POINT TO THESE QUES-TIONS?
JUST WONDERING.

I NEVER THOUGHT I'D SAY THIS, BUT...

...I ACTUALLY MISS NUDGE'S RUN-ON MOUTH.
I MISS HER SMILE.

I'M SURE SHE'S FINE.
I MISS HER LAUGH.
GLOOM
SHE MADE HER CHOICE.
AND, LIKE, HER, I DON'T KNOW...
... GIRLINESS.

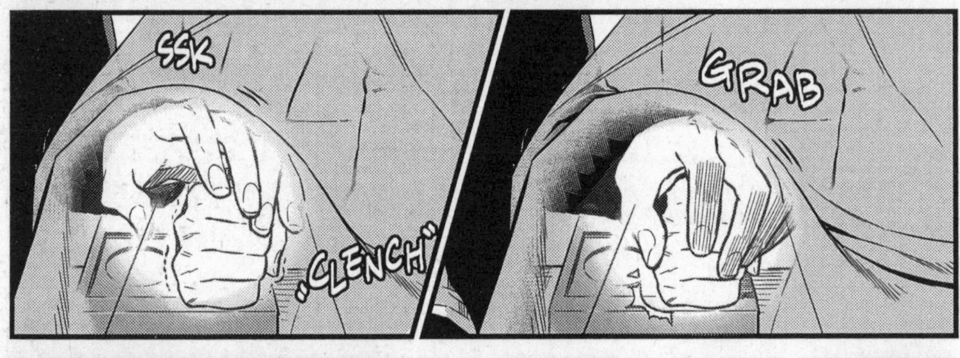
......
SSK
CLENCH
GRAB

......
!

SSK...

WE THINK IT WILL TAKE AT LEAST SEVEN DAYS...
... POSSIBLY MORE.
NO.
WE DON'T HAVE THAT MUCH TIME!
THEN THEY CAN'T COME.
BSSTC— BASIC SURVIVAL SKILLS TRAINING COURSE...
YOU CANNOT BOARD A VESSEL OF THE UNITED STATES NAVY UNLESS YOU SATISFACTORILY PASS ONE.
BUT—
THIS COURSE NORMALLY TAKES THREE WEEKS.
UNDER THESE EXTRAORDINARY CIRCUMSTANCES, WE CAN COMPACT IT INTO ONE WEEK.

IN THE EXTREMELY UNLIKELY EVENT THAT YOU LAST A WEEK, YOU MAY THEN BOARD A UNITED STATES NAVAL VESSEL...
...AND EXECUTE A RESCUE MISSION.

BUT ONLY ASTER YOU PASS A BS—

YEAH, WE GOT THE BS PART.
BUT LOOK, WE HAVE ALL THE SURVIVAL SKILLS WE NEED...AND THEN SOME.
YOU GUYS JUST DON'T HAVE THAT MUCH TO TEACH US.

ENSIGN.
YES, MA'AM.
......
PLEASE SHOW OUR VISITORS—AND THEIR DOGS—TO THEIR QUARTERS.
FWIP

......
......
GUYS...
...WE NEED THEIR RESOURCES.
IF THEY DO AGREE TO HELP US...
...IT COULD MEAN THE DIFFERENCE BETWEEN LIFE AND DEATH.
...I'LL MAKE SOME PHONE CALLS, SEE WHAT I CAN DO.
IN THE MEANTIME, JUST DO WHAT THEY SAY.

THE NEXT DAY
THESE ARE YOUR UNIFORMS.
DO YOU HAVE A LOT OF EXPLOSIVES?
THIS IS NOT A GOOD COLOR FOR ME.

RIIIP!!
WH-WHAT ARE YOU DOING?!
YOU'RE DEFACING PROPERTY OF THE UNITED STATES NAVY!
TUG
WELL...

...WE GOTTA LET OUR WINGS OUT.
FWOOOSH!!

!!

AAACK!!

I'M LTC PALMER.
SHAKE
SHAKE
SHAKE
EXCUSE ME. WHAT DOES LTC STAND FOR?
LIEUTENANT COLONEL, KID. AND YOU SPEAK ONLY WHEN SPOKEN TO. YOU GOT THAT?

ANTSY ANTSY
BOLT

THIS IS TOTAL CRAP!
I CAN'T BELIEVE I'M SITTING AT A FREAKING DESK...
...WHEN MY MOM IS TIED UP ON A SUBMARINE SOMEWHERE!

SIT DOWN!

MAX...

......
FWUMP

......

SWISH

WHAM!!

DIDN'T MEAN TO SLAM YOU THAT HARD.
YOU OKAY? SORRY.
COUGH
COUGH

TH-THAT WAS A FLUKE.
I TOLD OL' PALMER THAT WE HAD A PRETTY GOOD HANDLE ON THIS...
...BUT I GUESS HE DIDN'T BELIEVE ME.
HUFF HUFF
I WAS GOING EASY ON YOU BECAUSE YOU'RE A KID.
BUT IF YOU WANT A FIGHT, I CAN FIGHT.
SHOOM
FWIP

GRAB

SWIRL!

GWAAAAAAH!
FWOOOOSH!!
DON'T HURT HIM TOO BAD, MAX.

IT'S NOT YOUR FAULT.
I'M GENETICALLY ENHANCED.
AND, YOU KNOW, RUTHLESS. PLUS, OF COURSE, MEANER THAN A RABID WOLVERINE.
FLAP...

ARE YOU OKAY?
NOD NOD NOD
DO YOU WANT TO TRY IT AGAINST ANY OF THEM?
Me! Me next!
SHAKE SHAKE SHAKE
GOOD CHOICE. THEN HOW ABOUT YOU GIVE US A CHECKMARK...
GRIN
MAXIMUM RIDE
...SAYING WE PASSED THE SELF-DEFENSE PART OF THE BS? OKAY?

THIS IS FUN!
BEAT YOU!
SHOOP!!
THIS IS TOO EASY!
THESE KIDS!

SO YOU'RE SAYING...

...THEY CAN EASILY RUN FOUR MILES CARRYING HEAVY PACKS?
YES, MA'AM.

THE EIGHT-YEAR-OLD BEAT YOUR BEST CADET IN HAND-TO-HAND COMBAT?

SO DID THE SIX-YEAR-OLD GIRL, MA'AM.
NOM
NOM

This is really yummy!
ACTUALLY, SHE BEAT THE INSTRUCTOR ALSO.
BEAM

AND ALL IN JUST TWO DAYS?
SO, LIKE, WE WANT TO THANK YOU FOR THIS GREAT EXPERIENCE...

...BUT NOW THAT WE'VE GONE THROUGH ALL YOUR BS...
...CAN WE GO RESCUE MY MOM?

...YES.
!

TOMORROW.
WHAT?!

WE'RE PUTTING YOU ON THE *USS MINNESOTA*...
IT'S ON ITS WAY HERE NOW FROM SAN DIEGO. IT WILL ARRIVE HERE AT OH-THREE-HUNDRED HOURS TOMORROW.
...WHICH IS A STATE-OF-THE-ART, VIRGINIA-CLASS NUCLEAR SUBMARINE WITH MANY ENHANCED OFFENSIVE AND DEFENSIVE CAPABILITIES.
IT WILL REFUEL AND BE READY TO DEPLOY AT OH-SIX-HUNDRED HOURS.
YOU WILL BE WAITING ON THE DOCK AT THAT TIME. IF YOU ARE TWO MINUTES LATE, IT WILL LEAVE WITHOUT YOU.
IN ADDITION, WHILE ON BOARD THE *USS MINNESOTA*, YOU WILL OBEY EVERY SENIOR OFFICER WITHOUT QUESTION...
...YOU WILL COMPORT YOURSELF WITH DECORUM AND MATURITY...
...AND YOU WILL DO NOTHING TO ENDANGER THE SHIP, ITS CARGO, OR ITS PERSONNEL.

FAILURE TO FOLLOW THESE RULES TO THE LETTER WILL RESULT IN YOUR BEING DISEMBARKED AT THE CLOSEST POSSIBLE LOCATION...
...AND THE MISSION WILL BE SCRUBBED.
DO I MAKE MYSELF PERFECTLY CLEAR?
......

NOD

OH-SIX-HUNDRED HOURS THEN.
DISMISSED.
GULP...

MOM...HANG IN THERE.
To be continued in MAXIMUM RIDE, Vol. 10!

MAXIMUM
RIDE

NOM
NOM

MAXIMUM RIDE Vol. 9
FANG Cat
MAX dog
NAREE 2015
Max is the best!
HI, NARAE LEE HERE.
I KNOW IT TOOK A WHILE FOR THE 9TH VOLUME TO COME OUT. T.T THANK YOU SO MUCH FOR WAITING AND BUYING THIS BOOK! ♥
I WAS WONDERING WHAT TO DRAW FOR THIS AFTERWORD PAGE, AND THEN I STARTED IMAGINING WHAT ANIMALS THE FLOCK WOULD BE IF THEY HADN'T BEEN BIRDS. I THOUGHT MAX WOULD BE A CUTE DOG AND FANG A COOL CAT, SO THAT'S WHAT I DREW! WHAT DO YOU THINK? LOL!
WILL BE HOPING TO SEE YOU AGAIN IN VOLUME 10!

MAXIMUM RIDE: THE MANGA

BASED ON THE NOVELS BY
JAMES PATTERSON

ART AND ADAPTATION

BACKGROUND ASSISTANCE

MINJOUNG KIM
SOHYEON KIM